SCHOLASTIC

MATHS
SATs TESTS
YEAR 3

Book End, Range Road, Witney, Oxfordshire, OX29 0YD

www.scholastic.co.uk

© 2018 Scholastic Ltd

123456789   8901234567

A British Library Cataloguing-in-Publication Data
A catalogue record for this book is available from the
British Library.

ISBN 978-1407-18299-5

Printed and bound by Ashford Colour Press

Authors

Ann Montague-Smith

Series consultant

Paul Hollin

Editorial team

Rachel Morgan, Jenny Wilcox, Mark Walker, Christine Vaughan
and Margaret Eaton

Illustrations

Tom Heard

Layout

Nicolle Thomas and Oxford Designers and
Illustrators

Cover illustrations

Istock/calvindexter and Tomek.gr / Shutterstock/Visual Generation

Acknowledgements

Extracts from Department for Education website ©
Crown Copyright. Reproduced under the terms of the
Open Government Licence (OGL). www.nationalarchives.
gov.uk/doc/open-government-licence/version/3/

Every effort has been made to trace copyright holders
for the works reproduced in this publication, and the
publishers apologise or any inadvertent omissions.

Contents
Mathematics: Year 3

About this book

This book provides you with practice papers to help support children with end-of-year tests and to assess which skills need further development.

Using the practice papers

The practice papers in this book can be used as you would any other practice materials. The children need to be familiar with specific test-focused skills, such as ensuring equipment functions properly, leaving questions if they seem too difficult, working at a suitable pace for the tests and checking through their work.

If you choose to use the papers for revising content rather than practising tests, do be aware of the time factor. These tests are short at only 30 or 40 minutes per paper, as they are testing the degree of competence children have.

Equipment

The following equipment will be needed for all test papers.

- pencil/black pen
- eraser

For papers 2 and 3 you may need:

- ruler (mm and cm)
- angle measurer / protractor
- set square

About the tests

Each maths test has three papers:

- Paper 1: arithmetic – these are context-free calculations. The children have 30 minutes to answer the questions. 40 marks are available.

- Paper 2 and Paper 3: reasoning – these are mathematical reasoning problems both in context and out of context. The children have 40 minutes per paper to answer the questions. 35 marks are available per paper.

The papers should be taken in order and children may have a break between papers. All of the tests broadly increase in difficulty as they progress, and it is not expected that all children will be able to answer all of the questions.

The marks available for each question are shown in the test paper next to each question and are also shown next to each answer in the mark scheme.

Advice for parents and carers

How this book will help

This book will support your child to get ready for the school-based end-of-year tests in maths. It provides valuable practice and help on the responses and content expected of Year 3 children aged 7–8 years.

In the weeks leading up to the school tests, your child may be given plenty of practice, revision and tips to give them the best possible chance to demonstrate their knowledge and understanding. It is helpful to try to practise outside of school and many children benefit from extra input. This book will help your child to prepare and build their confidence.

In this book you will find two mathematics tests. The layout and format of each test closely matches those used in the National Tests so your child will become familiar with what to expect and get used to the style of the tests. There is a comprehensive answer section and guidance about how to mark the questions.

Tips

- Make sure that you allow your child to take the test in a quiet environment where they are not likely to be interrupted or distracted.
- Make sure your child has a flat surface to work on, with plenty of space to spread out and good light.
- Emphasise the importance of reading and re-reading a question.
- These tests are similar to the ones your child will take in May in Year 6 and they therefore give you a good idea of strengths and areas for development. When you have found areas that require some more practice, it is useful to go over these again and practise similar types of question with your child.
- Go through the tests again together, identify any gaps in learning and address any misconceptions or areas of misunderstanding. If you are unsure of anything yourself, then make an appointment to see your child's teacher who will be able to help and advise further.
- Practising little and often will enable your child to build up confidence and skills over a period of time.

Advice for children

- Revise and practise regularly.
- Spend some time each week practising.
- Focus on the areas you are least confident in to get better.
- Get a good night's sleep and eat a healthy breakfast.
- Be on time for school.
- Make sure you have all the things you need.
- Avoid stressful situations before a test.
- If a questions asks you to 'Show your method' then there will be marks if you get the method correct even if your answer is wrong.
- Leave out questions you do not understand and come back to them when you have completed those you can do.
- Check that you haven't missed any questions or pages out.
- Try to spend the last five minutes checking your work. Do your answers look about right?
- If you have time to spare and have a few questions unanswered, just have a go – you don't lose marks for trying.

Test coverage

The test content is divided into strands and sub-strands. These are listed, for each question, in a table at the end of every test to allow tracking of difficulties. In a small number of cases, where practical equipment such as containers would be required, these aspects are not tested.

Strand	Sub-strand
Number and place value	counting (in multiples)
	read, write, order and compare numbers
	place value; Roman numerals
	identify, represent and estimate; rounding
	number problems
Addition, subtraction, multiplication and division (calculations)	add/subtract mentally
	add/subtract using written methods
	estimates, use inverses and check
	add/subtract to solve problems
	multiply/divide mentally
	multiply/divide using written methods
	solve problems (commutative, associative, distributive and all four operations)
Fractions	recognise, find, write, name and count fractions
	equivalent fractions
	comparing and ordering fractions
	add/subtract fractions
	solve problems with fractions and decimals
Measurement	compare, describe and order measures
	estimate, measure and read scales
	money
	telling time, ordering time, duration and units of time
	solve problems (money; length; mass/weight; capacity/volume)
Geometry – properties of shape	recognise and name common shapes
	describe properties and classify shapes
	draw and make shapes and relate 2D and 3D shapes (including nets)
	angles – measuring and properties
Geometry – position and direction	patterns
Statistics	interpret and represent data
	solve problems involving data

SCHOLASTIC National Curriculum SATs Tests

Mathematics

Test A

Instructions Test A: Paper 1

You **may not** use a calculator to answer any questions in this test.

Questions and answers

- You have **30 minutes** to complete this test.
- Work as quickly and carefully as you can.
- Put your answer in the box for each question.

- If you cannot do one of the questions, **go on to the next one**. You can come back to it later if you have time.
- If you finish before the end, **go back and check your work**.

Marks

- The number next to each box at the side of the page tells you the maximum number of marks for each question.
- In this test, some questions are worth **2 marks** each. You will be awarded 2 marks for a correct answer.
- You may get 1 mark for showing a formal method.

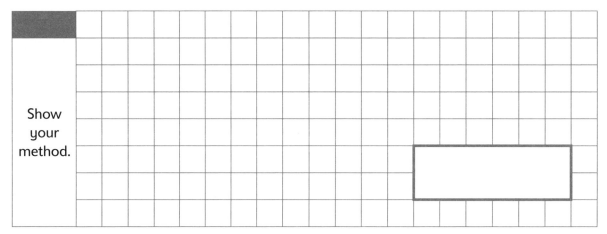

Show your method.

- All other questions are worth **1 mark** each.

■ SCHOLASTIC National Curriculum SATs Tests

1. 2 × 4 =

Marks

8

1

2. 16 − 9 =

7

1

3. 5 + 5 + 5 =

15

1

4. 145 + 5 =

Marks

150

1

5. 75 − 50 =

25

1

6. $\frac{1}{10} + \frac{1}{10} =$

$\frac{2}{10}$

1

7. $10 \times 8 =$

Marks

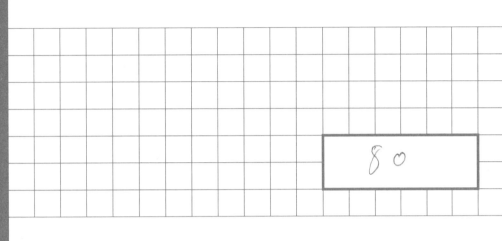

80

1

8. $12 \div 3 =$

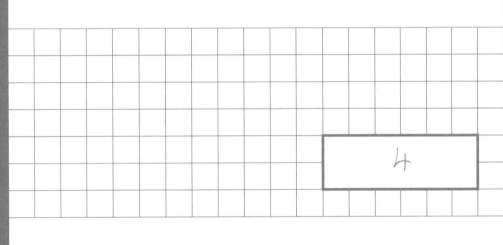

4

1

9. $9 + 19 =$

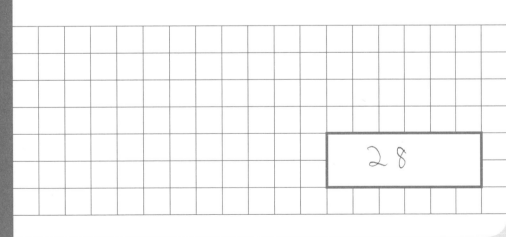

28

1

10. $60 + 60 =$

120

Marks

1

11. $\frac{3}{7} + \frac{2}{7} =$

$\frac{5}{7}$

1

12. $250 - 50 =$

200

1

13. 430 + 100 =

Marks

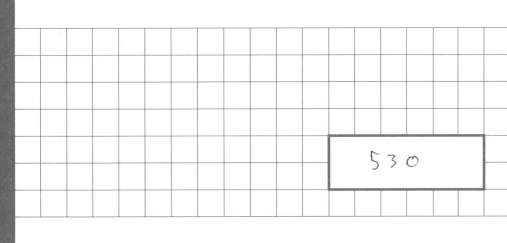

530

1

14. $\frac{1}{2}$ of 10 =

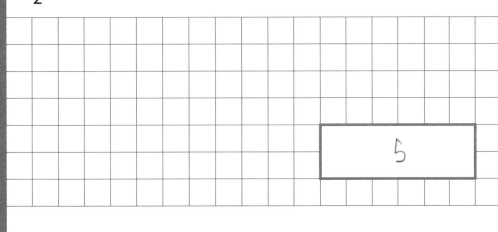

5

1

15. 89 + 27 =

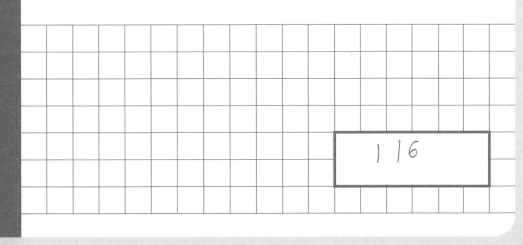

116

1

16.

$11 \times 3 =$

33

Marks

1

17.

$456 + 50 =$

506

1

18.

Show your method.

$$\begin{array}{r} 3\,{}^5\!6\,{}^1\!3 \\ -\ 1\ 4\ 7 \\ \hline 2\ 1\ 6 \end{array}$$

216

2

■SCHOLASTIC National Curriculum SATs Tests

19. $439 - 239 =$

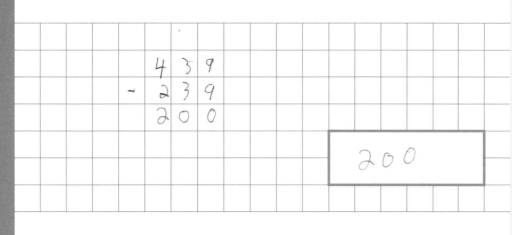

$$\begin{array}{r} 4\ 3\ 9 \\ -\ 2\ 3\ 9 \\ \hline 2\ 0\ 0 \end{array}$$

200

1

20. $0 \times 7 =$

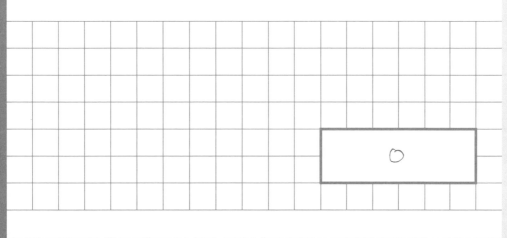

0

1

21. $92 - 45 =$

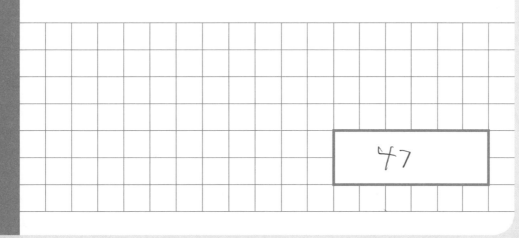

47

1

22. $456 + 65 =$

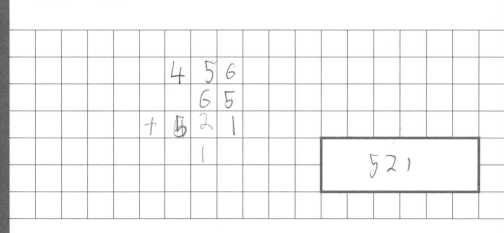

```
    4 5 6
      6 5
  +   2 1
      1
```

521

Marks

1

23. $\frac{1}{4}$ of $100 =$

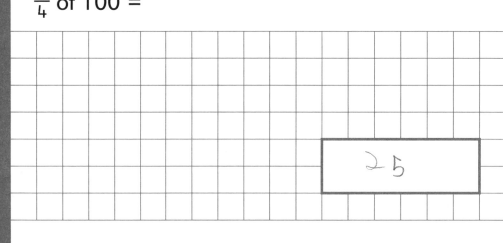

25

1

24. $245 - \underline{\qquad} = 90$

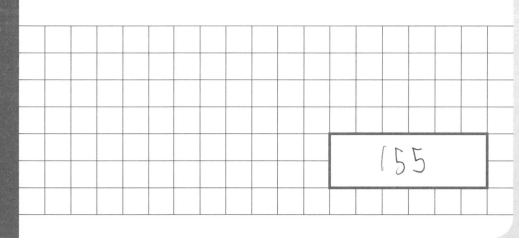

155

1

Marks

25. $\dfrac{7}{12} - \dfrac{3}{12} =$

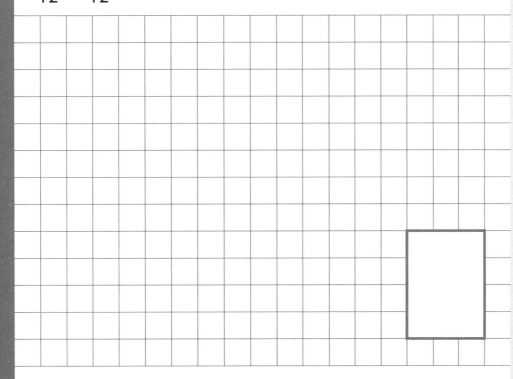

1

26. $463 + 500 =$

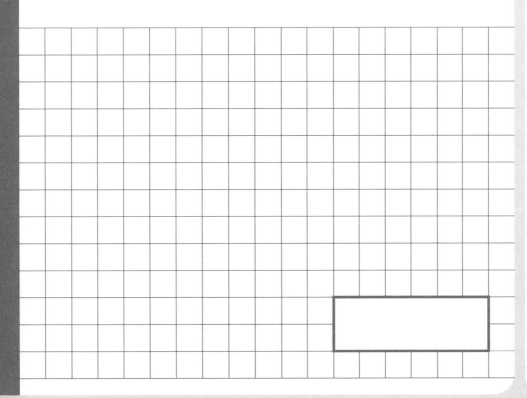

1

27. 36 × 4 =

Marks

Show your method.

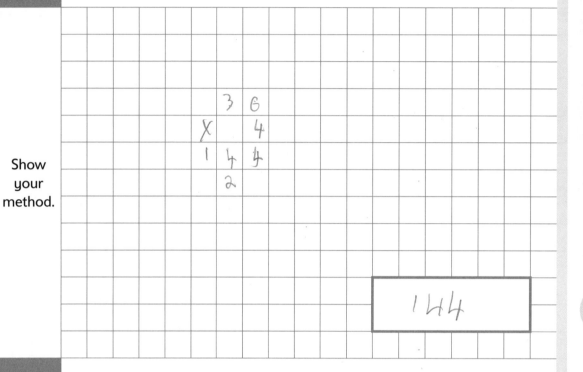

```
    3 6
  X   4
  1 4 4
    2
```

144

2

28. 1000 − 755 =

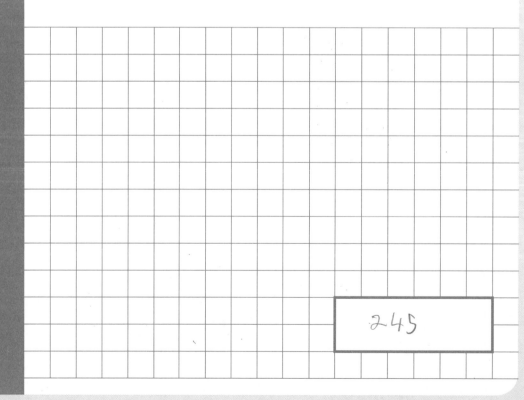

245

1

29. $153 \div 3 =$

Marks

Show your method.

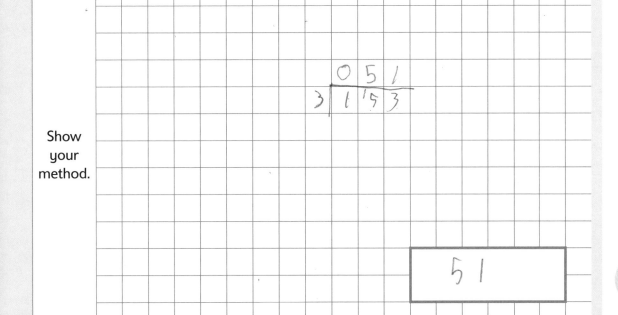

$$\begin{array}{r} 0\ 5\ 1 \\ 3\overline{\smash{)}1\ ^15\ 3} \end{array}$$

| 51 |

2

30. $30 \times 30 =$

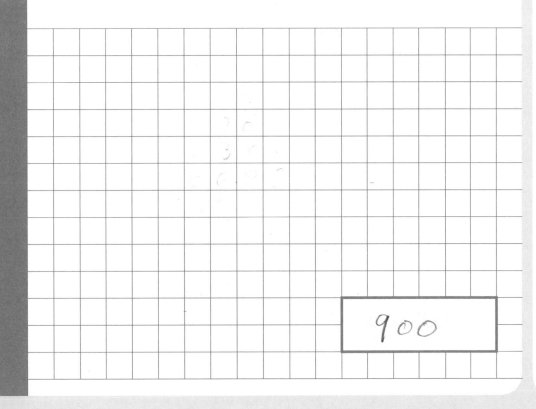

| 900 |

1

31.

Marks

Show your method.

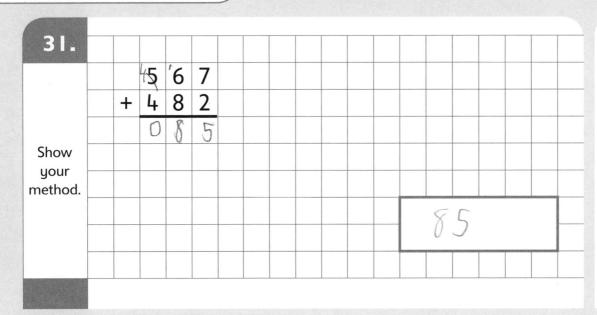

$$
\begin{array}{r}
{}^{4}5\,'6\,7 \\
+\ 4\ 8\ 2 \\
\hline
0\ 8\ 5
\end{array}
$$

85

2

32. 327 − 80 =

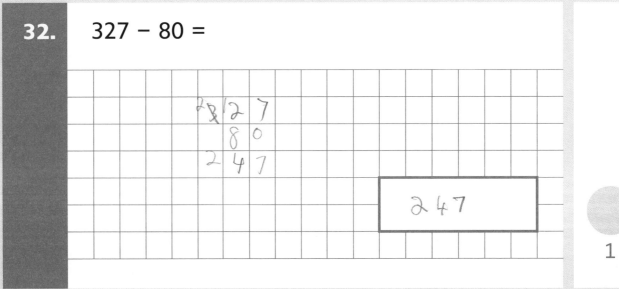

247

1

33. 60 ÷ 20 =

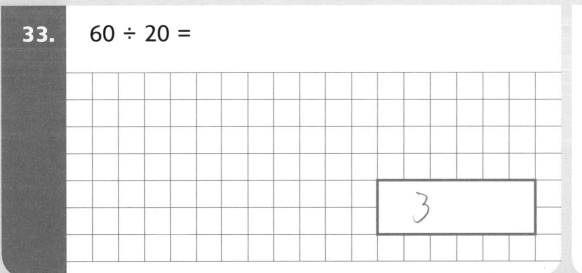

3

1

Marks

34. $347 + \underline{28} = 375$

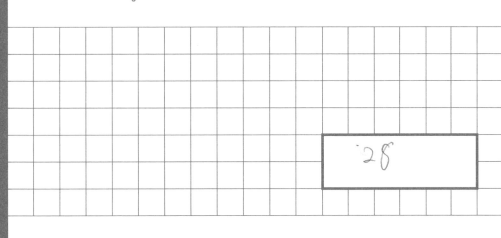

28

1

35. $\frac{2}{3}$ of 54 =

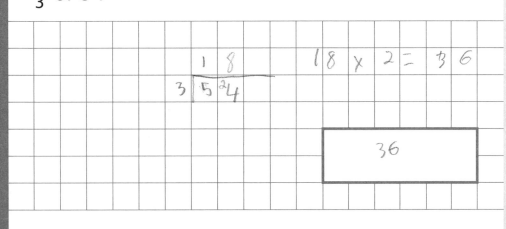

$18 \times 2 = 36$

36

1

36. $4 \times 13 \times 5 =$

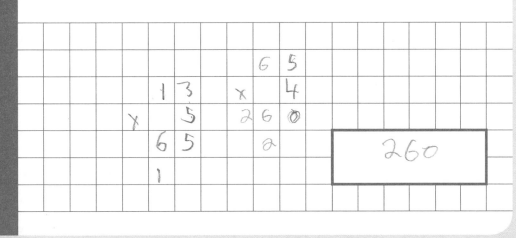

260

1

Test A: Paper 1 Marks

Q	Question	Possible marks	Actual marks
1	2×4	1	
2	$16 - 9$	1	
3	$5 + 5 + 5$	1	
4	$145 + 5$	1	
5	$75 - 50$	1	
6	$\frac{1}{10} + \frac{1}{10}$	1	
7	10×8	1	
8	$12 \div 3$	1	
9	$9 + 19$	1	
10	$60 + 60$	1	
11	$\frac{3}{7} + \frac{2}{7}$	1	
12	$250 - 50$	1	
13	$430 + 100$	1	
14	$\frac{1}{2}$ of 10	1	
15	$89 + 27$	1	
16	11×3	1	
17	$456 + 50$	1	
18	$\begin{array}{r} 3\,6\,3 \\ -\,1\,4\,7 \\ \hline \end{array}$	2	

Q	Question	Possible marks	Actual marks
19	$439 - 239$	1	
20	0×7	1	
21	$92 - 45$	1	
22	$456 + 65$	1	
23	$\frac{1}{4}$ of 100	1	
24	$245 - \underline{} = 90$	1	
25	$\frac{7}{12} - \frac{3}{12}$	1	
26	$463 + 500$	1	
27	36×4	2	
28	$1000 - 755$	1	
29	$153 \div 3$	2	
30	30×30	1	
31	$\begin{array}{r} 5\,6\,7 \\ +\,4\,8\,2 \\ \hline \end{array}$	2	
32	$327 - 80$	1	
33	$60 \div 20$	1	
34	$347 + \underline{} = 375$	1	
35	$\frac{2}{3}$ of 54	1	
36	$4 \times 13 \times 5$	1	
	Total	**40**	

24

SCHOLASTIC National Curriculum SATs Tests

Instructions Test A: Paper 2

- You have **40 minutes** for this test paper.
- You may **not use** a calculator to answer any questions in this test paper.
- Work as quickly and carefully as you can.
- Try to answer all the questions. If you cannot do one of the questions, **go on to the next one**. You can come back to it later, if you have time.
- If you finish before the end, **go back and check your work**.
- Ask your teacher if you are not sure what to do.

Follow the instructions for each question carefully.

If you need to do working out, you can use any space on the page – do not use rough paper.

Marks

Some questions have a method box like this.

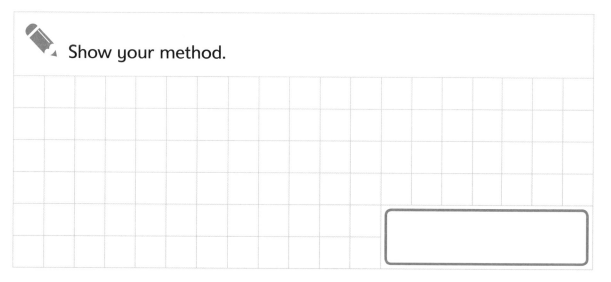

For these questions you may get a mark for showing your method.

The number on the right-hand side of the page tells you the maximum number of marks for each question.

1. Compare $\frac{1}{2}$ and $\frac{1}{4}$. Which fraction is bigger?

Marks

1

2. Join these shapes to their names.

Marks

Triangle

Square

Pentagon

Hexagon

1

3. What is the missing number in this pattern?

50,   60,   ☐ ,   80

Marks

1

SCHOLASTIC National Curriculum SATs Tests

Marks

4. There are 20 people on a bus.

$\frac{7}{10}$ of them are adults.

How many adults are on the bus?

1

5. What is the reading on the scale?

Marks

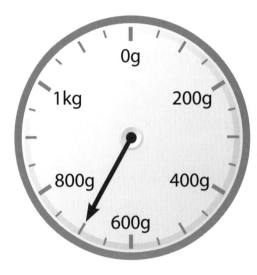

1

6. Estimate 356 + 57.

1

7. Draw two lines that are perpendicular to each other.

Marks

1

8. What is the perimeter of the square?

Marks

9cm

cm

1

9. Pippa is going on holiday for 3 weeks.

How many **days** will Pippa be on holiday?

Marks

days

1

10. John has six different hats and four different scarves.

How many different combinations of hats and scarves can John make?

🖋 Show your method.

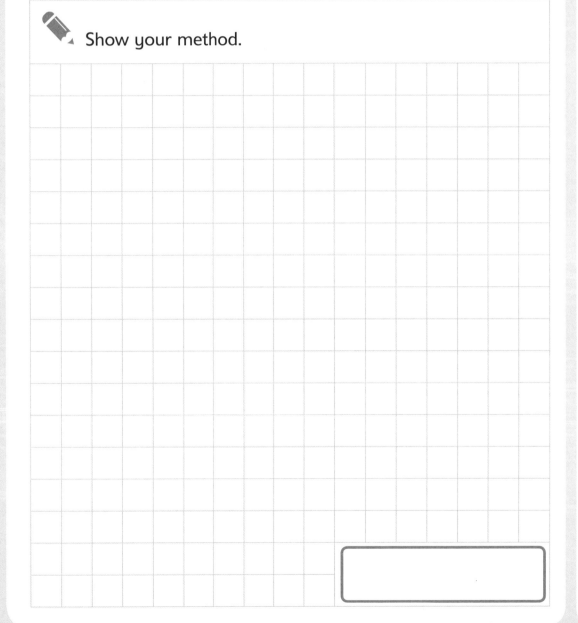

SCHOLASTIC National Curriculum SATs Tests

Marks

11. The bar chart shows the eye colour of children in Year 3.

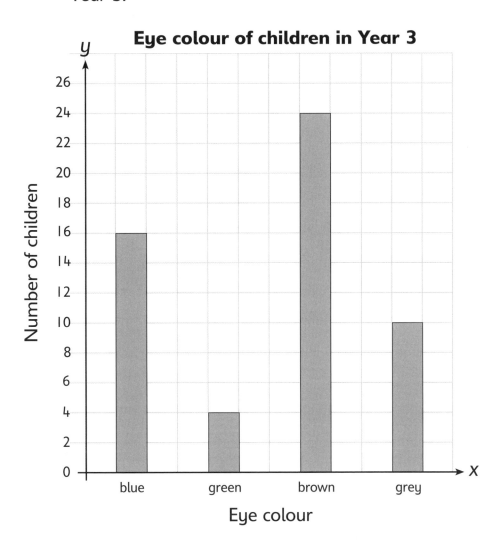

Eye colour of children in Year 3

How many more children have brown eyes than blue eyes?

1

How many fewer children have green eyes than grey eyes?

1

Marks

12. Here are two prices for the same phone.

£356   £256

Circle the phone that is cheaper.

1

What is the difference in price between the two phones?

1

Marks

13. Measure these lines with your ruler.

Decide which is longer.

Write its letter into the box.

A
_____

B
_____

1

How many more millimetres do I need to draw to make line A 10cm long?

mm

1

Marks

14. A 3D shape has five faces.

Three faces are rectangles.

Two faces are triangles.

What is the name of the shape?

1

Which 3D shape has six square faces?

1

SCHOLASTIC National Curriculum SATs Tests

15. There are 573 buttons in a box.

Another 265 buttons are added to the box.

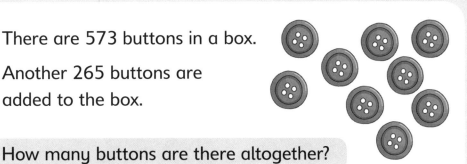

How many buttons are there altogether?

Marks

✏ Show your method.

buttons

2

16. At the farm there are 200 sheep, 120 cows and 7 goats.

How many animals are there in total?

Marks

✏ Show your method.

2

■SCHOLASTIC National Curriculum SATs Tests

17. Four children can fit into a people carrier.

What is the fewest number of people carriers needed to hold 72 children?

Show your method.

2

18. Myla and Jake collected this data about the types of vehicle that drove past their school.

Marks

Key: = three vehicles

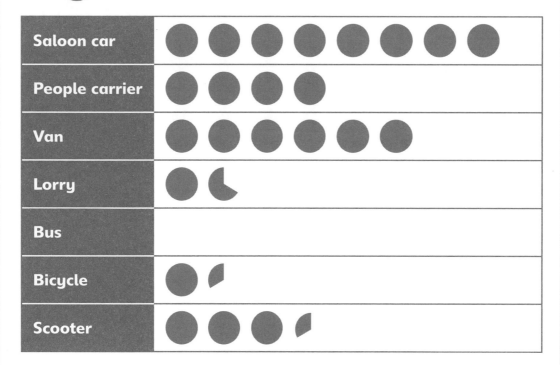

Saloon car	
People carrier	
Van	
Lorry	
Bus	
Bicycle	
Scooter	

There were three buses.

Draw the correct number of symbols to represent the buses.

1

The children saw ten of one type of vehicle.

Which vehicle was that?

1

19. The baker makes 12 rolls and puts them onto a tray.

He puts $\frac{3}{12}$ of the rolls onto a plate on display.

He puts $\frac{4}{12}$ of the rolls into a bag on the counter.

What fraction of the rolls is still on the tray?

Show your method.

Marks

2

20. Henry has 286 pieces in a modelling kit.

John has 579 pieces in his modelling kit.

They decide to put all the pieces together to make a very large model.

How many pieces do they have in total?

Show your method.

2

21. Tom buys two apples, a pack of juice and three biscuits.

How much change does Tom have from £5?

46p

57p

26p

✏️ Show your method.

£

Marks

2

22. Tammy has £67 to spend.

She decides to buy three DVDs that cost £17 each.

Then she buys two boxes of chocolates for £7 each.

How much money has she now?

Marks

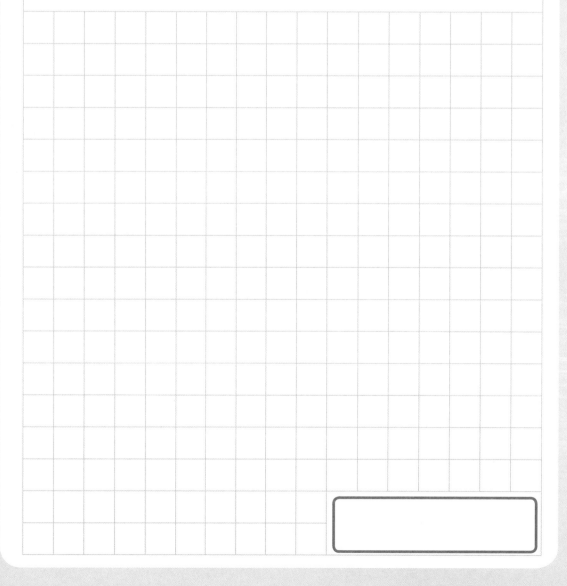

Show your method.

2

46

Q	Strand	Sub-strand	Possible marks	Actual marks
1	Fractions, decimals, percentages	Comparing and ordering fractions	1	
2	Geometry – properties of shapes	Recognise and name common shapes	1	
3	Number and place value	Identify, represent and estimate; rounding	1	
4	Fractions, decimals, percentages	Recognise, find, write, name and count fractions	1	
5	Measurement	Estimate, measure and read scales	1	
6	Calculations	Estimate, use inverses and check	1	
7	Geometry – properties of shapes	Describe properties and classify shapes	1	
8	Measurement	Perimeter, area	1	
9	Measurement	Telling time, ordering time, duration and units of time	1	
10	Calculations	Solve problems (commutative, associative, distributive and all four operations)	2	
11	Statistics	Solve problems involving data	2	
12	Number and place value	Number problems	2	
13	Measurement	Compare, describe and order measures	2	
14	Geometry – properties of shapes	Draw and make shapes and relate 2D to 3D shapes (including nets)	2	
15	Number and place value	Read, write, order and compare numbers	2	
16	Number and place value	Place value; Roman numerals	2	
17	Calculations	Multiply/divide using written methods	2	
18	Statistics	Interpret and represent data	2	
19	Fractions, decimals, percentages	Add/subtract fractions	2	
20	Calculations	Add/subtract using written methods	2	
21	Measurement	Solve problems (money; length; mass/weight; capacity/volume)	2	
22	Calculations	Multiply/divide using written methods	2	
		Total	35	

Instructions Test A: Paper 3

- You have **40 minutes** for this test paper.
- You may **not use** a calculator to answer any questions in this test paper.
- Work as quickly and carefully as you can.
- Try to answer all the questions. If you cannot do one of the questions, **go on to the next one**. You can come back to it later, if you have time.
- If you finish before the end, **go back and check your work**.
- Ask your teacher if you are not sure what to do.

Follow the instructions for each question carefully.

If you need to do working out, you can use any space on the page – do not use rough paper.

Marks

Some questions have a method box like this.

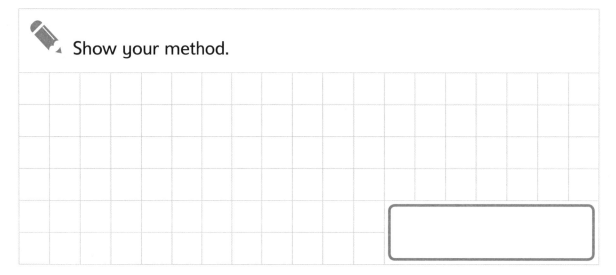

Show your method.

For these questions you may get a mark for showing your method.

The number on the right-hand side of the page tells you the maximum number of marks for each question.

1. Draw the next shape in this pattern.

Marks

1

2. How many squares make up a $\frac{1}{4}$ of this shape?

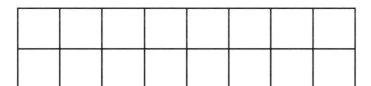

1

3. Write the next three numbers in this counting pattern.

Marks

400, 500, 600, 700, [   ], [   ], [   ]

1

4. Write the two missing digits to make this subtraction correct.

$$
\begin{array}{r}
9\ 7\ 1 \\
-\ \square\ \square\ 3 \\
\hline
5\ 0\ 8
\end{array}
$$

1

5. Look at the time on this clock. It is an evening time.

Write the time in digital format. Remember to use am or pm.

1

6. A sack of melons weighs 65kg.

Marks

If 37kg of melons are removed, what weight will be left in the sack?

kg

1

7. Here is a frequency chart for shoe colour in class 3.

Shoe colour	Tally	Frequency
Blue	|||	
Brown	~~||||~~		
Black	~~||||~~ ~~||||~~ ~~||||~~ ~~||||~~		
White	||||	

Write the total for each shoe colour in the table.

1

8. Which of these angles is greater than a right angle?

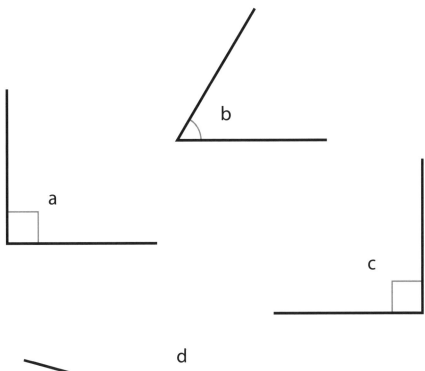

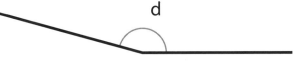

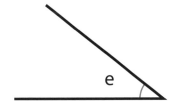

1

9. Find the missing number.

Marks

627 = 500 + _____ + 7

1

■SCHOLASTIC National Curriculum SATs Tests

10. What is two hundred and fifty-six add three hundred and sixty-four?

Marks

Show your method.

2

11. Which jug contains more water?

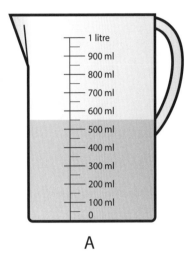

A

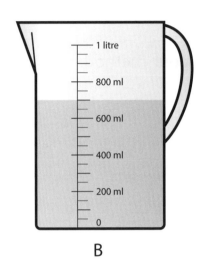

B

1

What is the difference in millilitres between the water levels in the jugs?

ml

1

12. There are 96 children waiting for assembly in a school hall. Two classes arrive late and the total increases to 151 children.

How many children arrive late?

✏ Show your method.

children

2

13. What is the difference between $\frac{8}{12}$ and $\frac{5}{12}$?

✏️ Show your method.

2

Marks

14. The table shows how much money the children at Oakdene School raised for charity.

January	February	March	April	May	June
£6	£15	£19	£12	£8	£18

How much more was raised in March than in January?

£

1

How much money was raised altogether?

£

1

15. Pens cost 28p each.

If Jane buys three pens how much change will she receive from £1?

Show your method.

p

2

16. Draw a triangle with one right angle.

Marks

Use your protractor and a ruler.

Make the horizontal and vertical sides 7cm long.

2

Marks

17. Sally drew a number line.

She wrote 51 at the beginning of the line.

She counted **on** 4 and wrote the number.

She did this two more times.

What are the numbers that Sally wrote?

1

Sally then wrote 51 at the beginning of the line.

She counted **backwards** by 4 and wrote the number.

She did this two more times.

What are the numbers that Sally wrote?

1

18. On Monday Tony eats $\frac{3}{9}$ of a bar of chocolate.

On Tuesday he eats $\frac{4}{9}$ of the bar of chocolate.

What fraction of the bar of chocolate is left?

Show your method.

Marks

2

Marks

19. There are 924 litres of orange juice.

365 litres are sold.

How many litres are left?

✏ Show your method.

litres

2

SCHOLASTIC National Curriculum SATs Tests

20. A very large package is delivered to the factory.

It weighs 879kg.

100kg is taken out of the package.

Another 10kg is put into the package.

How much does the package weigh now?

Marks

Show your method.

kg

2

Marks

21. A sheet of paper has a length of 30cm and a width of 210mm.

What is its perimeter in centimetres?

Show your method.

cm

2

22. Harper buys four packs of silver beads and three packs of gold beads.

What is the total number of beads?

16 gold beads

24 silver beads

✏ Show your method.

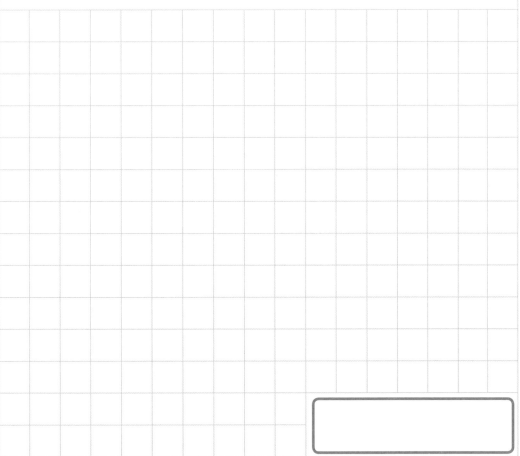

2

Test A: Paper 3 Marks

Q	Strand	Sub-strand	Possible marks	Actual marks
1	Geometry – position and direction	Patterns	1	
2	Fractions, decimals, percentages	Recognise, find, write, name and count fractions	1	
3	Number and place value	Counting (in multiples)	1	
4	Calculations	Estimate, use inverses and check	1	
5	Measurement	Telling time, ordering time, duration and units of time	1	
6	Measurement	Solve problems (money; length; mass/weight; capacity/volume)	1	
7	Statistics	Interpret and represent data	1	
8	Geometry – properties of shapes	Angles – measuring and properties	1	
9	Number and place value	Place value; Roman numerals	1	
10	Calculations	Add/subtract using written methods	2	
11	Measurement	Compare, describe and order measures	2	
12	Calculations	Add/subtract to solve problems	2	
13	Fractions, decimals, percentages	Add/subtract fractions	2	
14	Statistics	Solve problems involving data	2	
15	Calculations	Multiply/divide using written methods	2	
16	Geometry – properties of shapes	Draw and make shapes and relate 2D to 3D shapes (including nets)	2	
17	Number and place value	Identify, represent and estimate; rounding	2	
18	Fractions, decimals, percentages	Solve problems with fractions and decimals	2	
19	Calculations	Add/subtract using written methods	2	
20	Number and place value	Number problems	2	
21	Measurement	Perimeter, area	2	
22	Calculations	Multiply/divide using written methods	2	
		Total	35	

■SCHOLASTIC National Curriculum SATs Tests

Mathematics

Test B

Instructions Test B: Paper 1

You **may not** use a calculator to answer any questions in this test.

Questions and answers

- You have **30 minutes** to complete this test.
- Work as quickly and carefully as you can.
- Put your answer in the box for each question.

- If you cannot do one of the questions, **go on to the next one**. You can come back to it later if you have time.
- If you finish before the end, **go back and check your work**.

Marks

- The number next to each box at the side of the page tells you the maximum number of marks for each question.
- In this test, some questions are worth **2 marks** each. You will be awarded 2 marks for a correct answer.
- You may get 1 mark for showing a formal method.

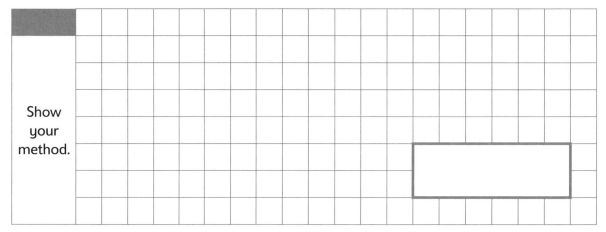

Show your method.

- All other questions are worth **1 mark** each.

Marks

1.   6 + 19 =

1

2.   4 + 4 + 4 + 4 =

1

3.   38 − 20 =

1

4. $\frac{1}{2}$ of 30 =

Marks

1

5. 500 + 300 =

1

6. 22 ÷ 2 =

1

Marks

7. $\frac{1}{5} + \frac{3}{5} =$

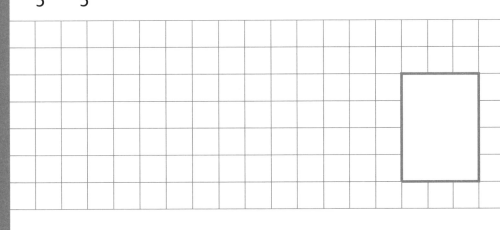

1

8. $5 \times 9 =$

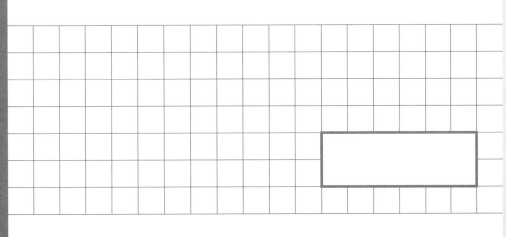

1

9. $64 + 8 =$

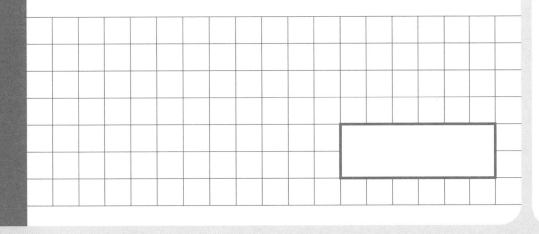

1

10. 22 × 3 =

Marks

1

11. 43 + _____ = 60

1

12. 45 ÷ 3 =

1

SCHOLASTIC National Curriculum SATs Tests

13. 10 × 38 =

Marks

1

14. 361 − 70 =

1

15. $\frac{3}{4}$ of 12 =

1

16. $296 - 100 =$

Marks

1

17. $\frac{5}{6} - \frac{2}{6} =$

1

18. $90 + 365 =$

1

19. $\frac{1}{8} + \frac{4}{8} + \frac{2}{8} =$

Marks

1

20. $100 \times 3 \times 2 =$

1

21. $155 + 38 =$

1

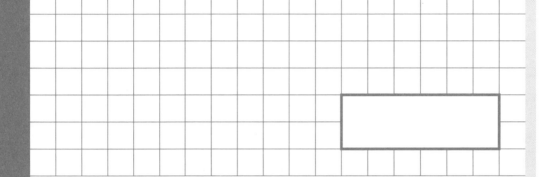
22. 1000 − _____ = 450

Marks

1

23. 300 + 270 + 9 =

1

24. 64 ÷ _____ = 8

1

25.

Marks

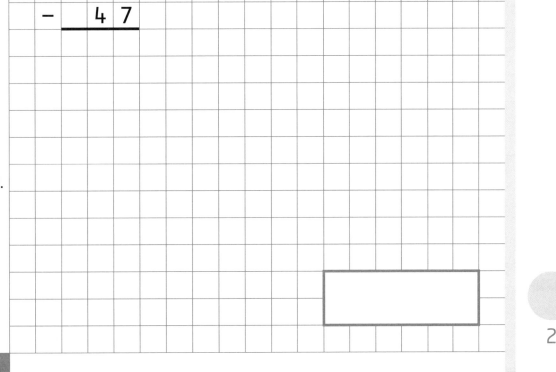

$$
\begin{array}{r}
1\ 3\ 5 \\
-\ \ \ 4\ 7 \\
\hline
\end{array}
$$

Show your method.

2

26. 110 + 220 + 330 =

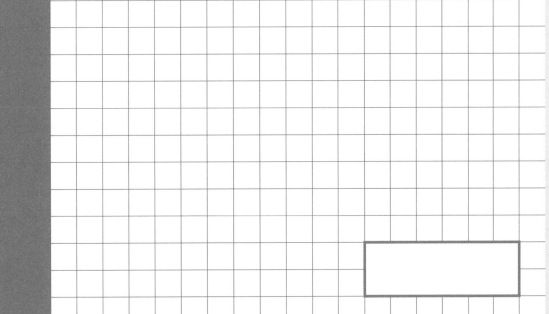

1

27. $1000 - 993 =$

Marks

1

28.

Show your method.

$$
\begin{array}{r}
5\ 6\ 2 \\
+\ 2\ 7\ 9 \\
\hline
\end{array}
$$

2

29. $8 + 80 + 800 =$

1

 SCHOLASTIC National Curriculum SATs Tests

30. $\frac{1}{2}$ of 700 =

Marks

1

31.

$$
\begin{array}{r}
1\ 4\ 6 \\
\times\quad\ \ 4 \\
\hline
\end{array}
$$

Show your method.

2

32. 70 − 38 + 68 =

Marks

1

33. $\frac{7}{9} - \frac{5}{9} =$

1

34.

Show your method.

5 ⟌ 7 3 5

2

SCHOLASTIC National Curriculum SATs Tests

35. $67 \times 5 \times 2 =$

1

36. $\frac{3}{10}$ of 60 =

1

Test B: Paper 1 Marks

Q	Question	Possible marks	Actual marks
1	6 + 19	1	
2	4 + 4 + 4 + 4	1	
3	38 − 20	1	
4	$\frac{1}{2}$ of 30	1	
5	500 + 300	1	
6	22 ÷ 2	1	
7	$\frac{1}{5} + \frac{3}{5}$	1	
8	5 × 9	1	
9	64 + 8	1	
10	22 × 3	1	
11	43 + ___ = 60	1	
12	45 ÷ 3	1	
13	10 × 38	1	
14	361 − 70	1	
15	$\frac{3}{4}$ of 12	1	
16	296 − 100	1	
17	$\frac{5}{6} - \frac{2}{6}$	1	
18	90 + 365	1	

Q	Question	Possible marks	Actual marks
19	$\frac{1}{8} + \frac{4}{8} + \frac{2}{8}$	1	
20	100 × 3 × 2	1	
21	155 + 38	1	
22	1000 − ___ = 450	1	
23	300 + 270 + 9	1	
24	64 ÷ ___ = 8	1	
25	$\begin{array}{r} 1\ 3\ 5 \\ -\ \ \ 4\ 7 \\ \hline \end{array}$	2	
26	110 + 220 + 330	1	
27	1000 − 993	1	
28	$\begin{array}{r} 5\ 6\ 2 \\ +\ 2\ 7\ 9 \\ \hline \end{array}$	2	
29	8 + 80 + 800	1	
30	$\frac{1}{2}$ of 700	1	
31	$\begin{array}{r} 1\ 4\ 6 \\ \times\ \ \ \ 4 \\ \hline \end{array}$	2	
32	70 − 38 + 68	1	
33	$\frac{7}{9} - \frac{5}{9}$	1	
34	$5\overline{)7\ 3\ 5}$	2	
35	67 × 5 × 2	1	
36	$\frac{3}{10}$ of 60	1	
	Total	**40**	

Instructions Test B: Paper 2

- You have **40 minutes** for this test paper.
- You may **not use** a calculator to answer any questions in this test paper.
- Work as quickly and carefully as you can.
- Try to answer all the questions. If you cannot do one of the questions, **go on to the next one**. You can come back to it later, if you have time.
- If you finish before the end, **go back and check your work**.
- Ask your teacher if you are not sure what to do.

Follow the instructions for each question carefully.

If you need to do working out, you can use any space on the page – do not use rough paper.

Marks

Some questions have a method box like this.

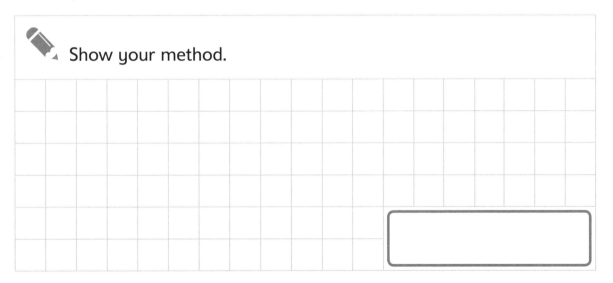

For these questions you may get a mark for showing your method.

The number on the right-hand side of the page tells you the maximum number of marks for each question.

1. Continue the pattern.

Marks

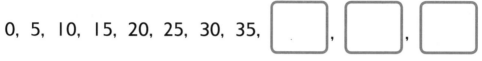

0, 5, 10, 15, 20, 25, 30, 35, ⬜, ⬜, ⬜

1

2. Circle half of these beads.

1

3. Write the two missing digits to make this addition correct.

$$
\begin{array}{r}
6\ 4\ 0 \\
+\ 1\ \square\ 7 \\
\hline
\square\ 2\ 7
\end{array}
$$

1

4. It is time for afternoon break. What time does the clock show?

Marks

1

Marks

5. How many thirds are shaded?

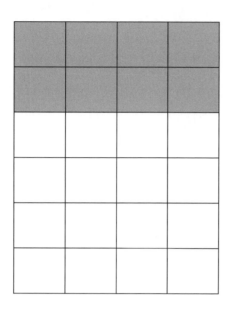

1

6. What is 7cm and 3mm add 4cm and 6mm?

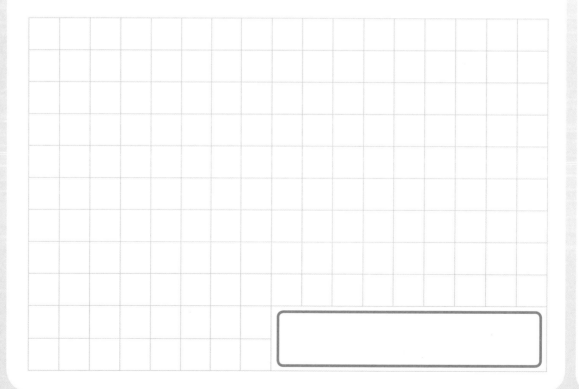

1

7. Which of these angles is a right angle?

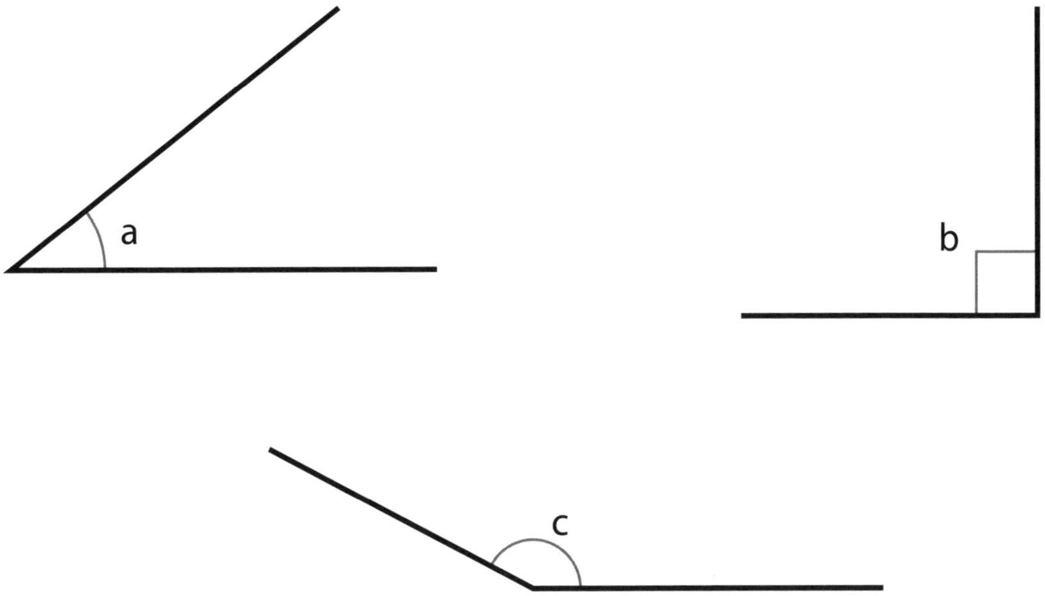

Marks

a

b

c

1

8. In the school's library, there are 500 fiction books, 160 non-fiction books and 9 reference books.

Marks

How many books are there in the library?

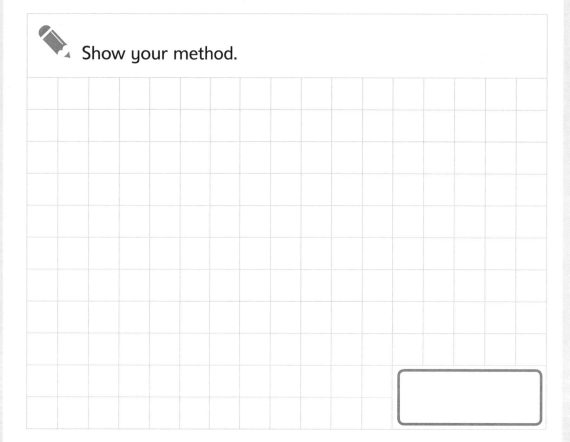

Show your method.

2

9. Anna has 192 cakes to sell as a charity cake sale. She sells 48 cakes in the first two hours.

How many cakes does Anna have left?

Marks

Show your method.

2

10. Complete these statements.

Use < and >.

450g ☐ 540g

25cm ☐ 115mm

Marks

1

11. Stephen has a bag of raisins.

The label says there are 145 raisins in the bag.

Stephen eats several handfuls of raisins, then counts the remainder.

If there are 68 raisins left, how many has Stephen eaten?

Marks

Show your method.

raisins

2

12. Write these fractions in order of size.

Start with the smallest.

$\dfrac{7}{8}$

$\dfrac{3}{8}$

$\dfrac{1}{8}$

$\dfrac{6}{8}$

Marks

1

Marks

13. This table shows the favourite fruits of some children.

Fruit	Number of children
Apples	20
Pears	10
Oranges	13
Bananas	15
Kiwi	5
Mango	8
Dates	2

How many more children like the most popular fruit than like the least popular fruit?

1

Which fruit is more popular than pears but not as popular as bananas?

1

14. These stop clocks show how long it took Mark and Gemma to read a story.

Marks

Mark

Gemma

Who took the longest to read the story?

1

How many more minutes did it take to read the story?

minutes

1

Marks

15. Join these shapes to their properties.

Has six square faces

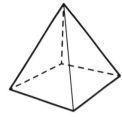

Has twelve edges and six
rectangular faces

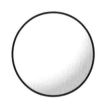

Four of its faces meet
at a vertex

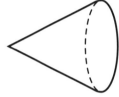

Has one curved face

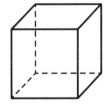

Has a circle for its base

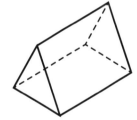

Has two triangular faces and
three rectangular faces

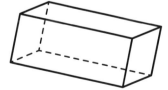

2

16. A hundred square starts at 1 and finishes at 100.

Charlie and Dan count along a hundred square.

Charlie counts in 4s.

Dan counts in 5s.

Which boy will say more numbers?

Show your method.

Marks

2

Marks

17. There are 16 chocolates in a box.

$\frac{5}{8}$ of the box of chocolates is eaten.

How many chocolates are left?

Show your method.

chocolates

2

18. These are the ingredients for making 12 biscuits.

B

INGREDIENTS

28g sugar

84g flour

56g butter

Write the ingredients for making six biscuits.

| | g | sugar |

| | g | flour |

| | g | butter |

2

SCHOLASTIC National Curriculum SATs Tests

19. At 9am there are 676 cars in a car park.

By midday, 250 cars have left the car park and 47 more had arrived.

How many cars are there now?

Marks

✎ Show your method.

cars

2

20. An electronic book reader measures 190mm in height and 11cm in width.

What is its perimeter in centimetres?

Marks

✏ Show your method.

cm

2

Marks

21. Pears cost 23p for a bag.

Apples cost 17p for a bag.

23p

17p

Marta buys three bags of pears and one bag of apples.

How much money does Marta spend?

Show your method.

2

Marks

22. The bar chart shows the average temperatures in Sydney, Australia, each month.

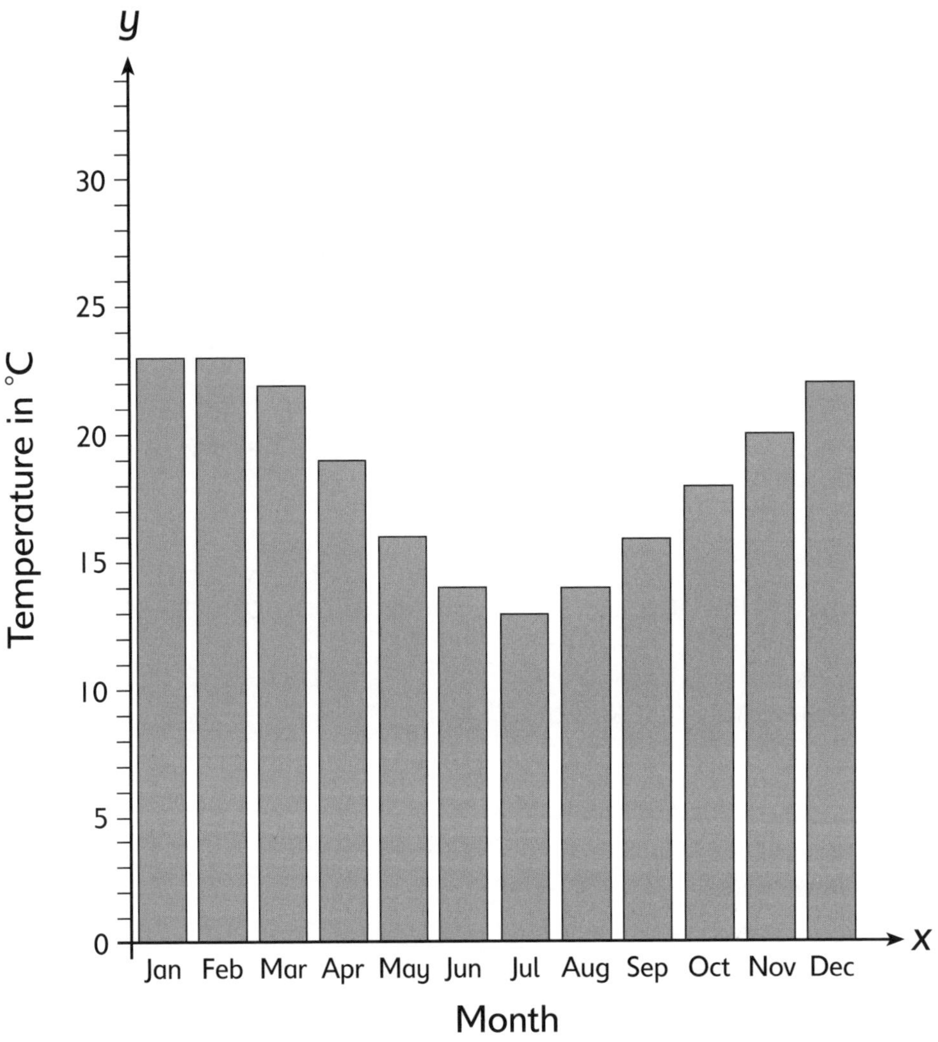

How much hotter is it in February than in June?

°C

1

How much cooler is it in May than in December?

°C

1

Q	Strand	Sub-strand	Possible marks	Actual marks
1	Geometry – position and direction	Patterns	1	
2	Fractions, decimals. percentages	Recognise, find, write, name and count fractions	1	
3	Calculations	Estimate, use inverses and check	1	
4	Measurement	Telling time, ordering time, duration and units of time	1	
5	Fractions, decimals. percentages	Equivalent fractions	1	
6	Measurement	Solve problems (money; length; mass/weight; capacity/volume)	1	
7	Geometry – properties of shapes	Angles – measuring and properties	1	
8	Number and place value	Place value; Roman numerals	2	
9	Calculations	Add/subtract using written methods	2	
10	Measurement	Compare, describe and order measures	1	
11	Calculations	Add/subtract to solve problems	2	
12	Fractions, decimals. percentages	Comparing and ordering fractions	1	
13	Statistics	Interpret and represent data	2	
14	Measurement	Telling time, ordering time, duration and units of time	2	
15	Geometry – properties of shapes	Draw and make shapes and relate 2D to 3D shapes (including nets)	2	
16	Number and place value	Identify, represent and estimate; rounding	2	
17	Fractions, decimals. percentages	Solve problems with fractions and decimals	2	
18	Calculations	Solve problems (commutative, associative, distributive and all four operations)	2	
19	Calculations	Number problems	2	
20	Measurement	Perimeter, area	2	
21	Calculations	Multiply/divide using written methods	2	
22	Statistics	Solve problems involving data	2	
		Total	**35**	

Instructions Test B: Paper 3

- You have **40 minutes** for this test paper.
- You may **not use** a calculator to answer any questions in this test paper.
- Work as quickly and carefully as you can.
- Try to answer all the questions. If you cannot do one of the questions, **go on to the next one**. You can come back to it later, if you have time.
- If you finish before the end, **go back and check your work**.
- Ask your teacher if you are not sure what to do.

Follow the instructions for each question carefully.

If you need to do working out, you can use any space on the page – do not use rough paper.

Marks

Some questions have a method box like this.

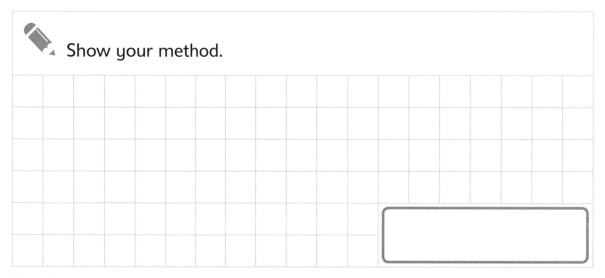

Show your method.

For these questions you may get a mark for showing your method.

The number on the right-hand side of the page tells you the maximum number of marks for each question.

1. Which clock shows half-past two?
Circle the correct letter.

Marks

A

B

C

D

1

2. The pictogram shows Class 4's favourite fruit.

Marks

Our favourite fruit

Key:  = one child

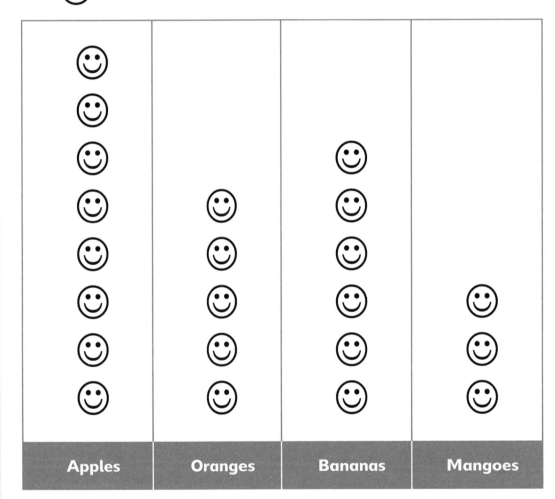

| Apples | Oranges | Bananas | Mangoes |

How many more children like bananas than oranges?

1

3. What is the capacity of this jug?

Marks

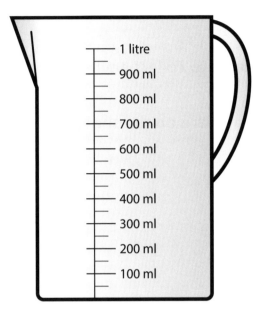

1

4. Mum, Dad, Michael and Lorna go to the supermarket with a shopping list.

They decide to split the list equally between them to make it quicker.

They have 14 items to collect each.

How many items were on the shopping list?

Marks

1

■SCHOLASTIC National Curriculum SATs Tests

5. What is the perimeter of this garden?

12m

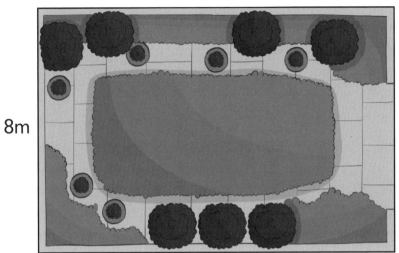

8m

m

1

Marks

6. This bar chart shows what pets the children in Class 3 have.

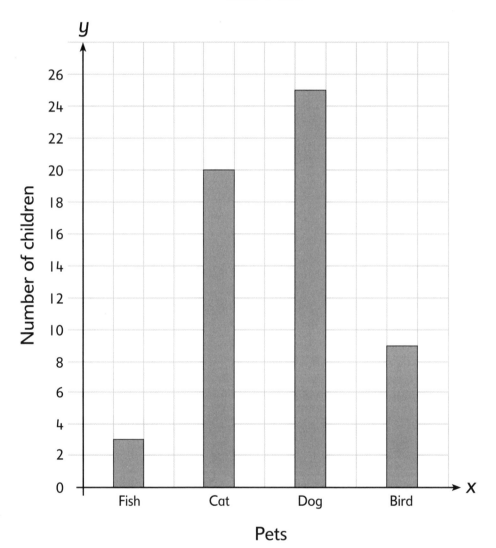

Our Pets

How many children have birds as pets?

1

SCHOLASTIC National Curriculum SATs Tests

7. Four children each put 13p in a purse.

How much money is that altogether?

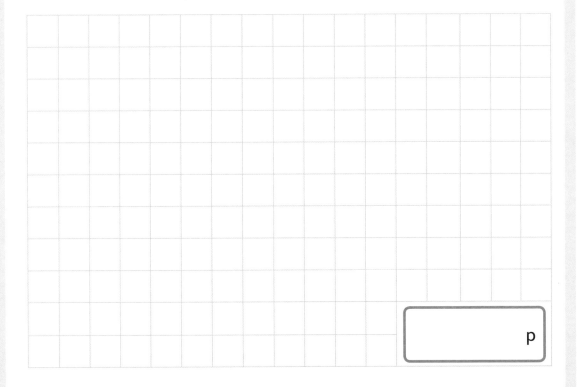

p

Marks

1

8. What is 10 less than 406?

1

9. Joanne says that 151 + 68 = 219

Use a subtraction calculation to check if she is right, then write yes or no in the box.

Marks

1

10. Write these fractions in order. Start with the smallest.

$$\frac{5}{10} \qquad \frac{3}{10} \qquad \frac{1}{10} \qquad \frac{9}{10} \qquad \frac{2}{10}$$

1

SCHOLASTIC National Curriculum SATs Tests

11. Write the two missing digits to make this addition correct.

$$
\begin{array}{r}
\boxed{}\,8\,\boxed{} \\
+\quad 4\ \ 5 \\
\hline
2\ \ 3\ \ 2
\end{array}
$$

1

12. Here is a 2D shape.

Marks

Write **horizontal** by the horizontal line.

1

Write **vertical** next to the vertical line.

1

13. What is 500 add 70 add 8?

Marks

1

Write the missing numbers.

140,   240,   [   ] ,   [   ] ,   540

1

Marks

14. What is $\frac{3}{8}$ of 24?

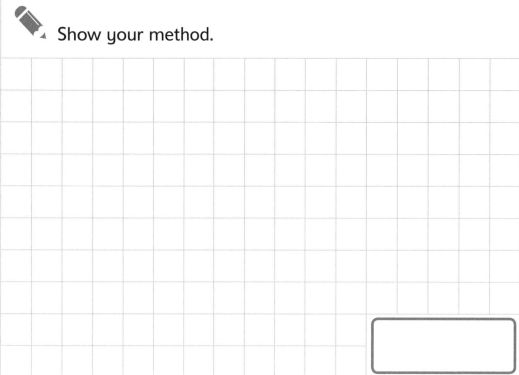

Show your method.

2

SCHOLASTIC National Curriculum SATs Tests

15. Write the measurement where the arrows point on the ruler.

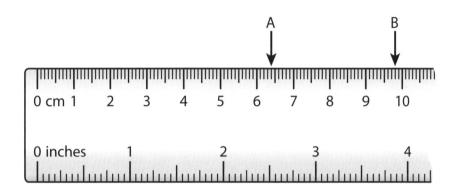

A

| cm | mm |

1

B

| cm | mm |

1

16. What is four hundred and sixty-five minus one hundred and eighty-seven?

Marks

✏ Show your method.

2

Marks

17. A cake is cut into ten equal slices.

If four slices are eaten, what fraction of the cake is left? Give your answer as a fraction in its simplest form.

✎ Show your method.

2

18. Look at this pair of scissors.

Now look at these pictures.

a  b  c

Marks

Which picture shows that the scissors have turned clockwise through one right angle?

1

Which picture shows that the scissors have turned clockwise through three right angles?

1

19. What is the product of 27 and 8?

Marks

✏️ Show your method.

2

20. There are 263 children who eat packed lunches at school.

Another 167 children eat school dinners.

How many children is that in total?

Marks

✏ Show your method.

2

Marks

21. A pizza has been cut into ten pieces.

Josh takes $\frac{3}{10}$ of the pizza.

Mark takes $\frac{4}{10}$ of the pizza.

Maria takes two slices of pizza.

What fraction of the pizza is left?

Show your method.

2

22.

Jon has 452 marbles that are red, green and blue.

He drops the marbles on the floor.

Then he starts to pick them up.

300 are red.

12 are green.

How many marbles are blue?

Marks

✏ Show your method.

2

Marks

23. The car holds 60 litres of fuel.

At the beginning of the week the tank is full.

On Wednesday the tank has 36 litres of fuel added to fill it up.

On Friday another 36 litres of fuel is added so that it is full.

On Saturday another 23 litres is added to fill it up.

How much fuel is used during this week?

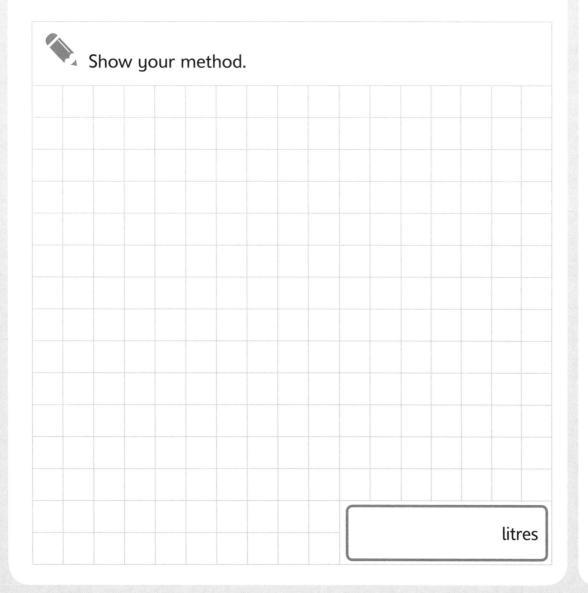

Show your method.

litres

2

Test B: Paper 3 Marks

Q	Strand	Sub-strand	Possible marks	Actual marks
1	Measurement	Telling time, ordering time, duration and units of time	1	
2	Statistics	Interpret and represent data	1	
3	Measurement	Compare, describe and order measures	1	
4	Calculations	Solve problems (commutative, associative, distributive and all four operations)	1	
5	Measurement	Perimeter, area	1	
6	Statistics	Solve problems involving data	1	
7	Calculations	Multiply/divide using written methods	1	
8	Number and place value	Read, write, order and compare numbers	1	
9	Calculations	Estimate, use inverses and check	1	
10	Fractions, decimals, percentages	Recognise, find, write name and count fractions	1	
11	Calculations	Add/subtract to solve problems	1	
12	Geometry – properties of shapes	Describe properties and classify shapes	2	
13	Number and place value	Identify, represent and estimate; rounding	2	
14	Fractions, decimals, percentages	Comparing and ordering fractions	2	
15	Measurement	Estimate, measure and read scales	2	
16	Calculations	Add/subtract using written methods	2	
17	Fractions, decimals, percentages	Equivalent fractions	2	
18	Geometry – properties of shapes	Angles – measuring and properties	2	
19	Calculations	Multiply/divide using written methods	2	
20	Calculations	Add/subtract using written methods	2	
21	Fractions, decimals, percentages	Add/subtract fractions	2	
22	Number and place value	Place value; Roman numerals	2	
23	Measurement	Solve problems (money; length; mass/weight; capacity/volume)	2	
		Total	35	

■SCHOLASTIC National Curriculum SATs Tests

Marks & guidance

Marking and assessing the papers

The mark schemes provide details of correct answers including guidance for questions that have more than one mark.

Interpreting answers

The guidance below should be followed when deciding whether an answer is acceptable or not. As general guidance, answers should be unambiguous.

Problem	Guidance
The answer is equivalent to the one in the mark scheme.	The mark scheme will generally specify which equivalent responses are allowed. If this is not the case, award the mark unless the mark scheme states otherwise. For example: 1 ½ or 1.5
The answer is correct but the wrong working is shown.	A correct response will always be marked as correct.
The correct response has been crossed (or rubbed) out and not replaced.	Do not award the mark(s) for legible crossed-out answers that have not been replaced or that have been replaced by a further incorrect attempt.
The answer has been worked out correctly but an incorrect answer has been written in the answer box.	Where appropriate follow the guidance in the mark scheme. If no guidance is given then: ● award the mark if the incorrect answer is due to a transcription error ● award the mark if there is extra unnecessary workings which do not contradict work already done ● do not award the mark if there is extra unnecessary workings which do contradict work already done.
More than one answer is given.	If all answers are correct (or a range of answers is given, all of which are correct), the mark will be awarded unless specified otherwise by the mark schemes. If both correct and incorrect responses are given, no mark will be awarded.

Problem	Guidance
There appears to be a misread of numbers affecting the working.	In general, the mark should not be awarded. However, in two-mark questions that have a working mark, award one mark if the working is applied correctly using the misread numbers, provided that the misread numbers are comparable in difficulty to the original numbers. For example, if '243' is misread as '234', both numbers may be regarded as comparable in difficulty.
No answer is given in the expected place, but the correct answer is given elsewhere.	Where an understanding of the question has been shown, award the mark. In particular, where a word or number response is expected, a pupil may meet the requirement by annotating a graph or labelling a diagram elsewhere in the question.

Formal written methods

The following guidance shows examples of formal written methods suitable for Year 3. These methods may not be used in all schools and any formal written method, which is the preferred method of the school and which gives the correct answer, should be acceptable.

Addition

64 + 25 becomes

```
    6  0  +  4
+   2  0  +  5
  ─────────────
    8  0  +  9
```

Answer: 89

57 + 29 becomes

```
    5  0  +     7
+   2  0  +     9
  ─────────────────
    7  0  +  1  6
```

Answer: 86

or

```
    5  7
+   2  9
  ───────
    8  6
    1
```

Answer: 86

135 + 287 becomes

```
    1  0  0  +     3  0  +     5
+   2  0  0  +     8  0  +     7
  ──────────────────────────────
    3  0  0  +  1  1  0  +  1  2
  ──────────────────────────────
    4  1  0           +  1  2
```

Answer: 422

or

```
    1  3  5
+   2  8  7
  ──────────
    4  2  2
    1  1
```

Answer: 422

Subtraction

94 − 33 becomes

```
    9  0  and  4
−   3  0  and  3
  ───────────────
    6  0  and  1
```

Answer: 61

or

```
    9  4
−   3  3
  ───────
    6  1
```

Answer: 61

85 − 37 becomes

```
    8  0  and     5
−   3  0  and     7
  ───────────────────
    7  0  and  1  5
    3  0  and     7
  ───────────────────
    4  0  and     8
```

Answer: 48

or

```
       70          1
    8̶  0̶  and     5
−   3  0  and     7
  ───────────────────
    4  0  and     8
```

Answer: 48

341 − 196 becomes

```
    3  0  0  and     4  0  and     1
−   1  0  0  and     9  0  and     6
  ──────────────────────────────────
    2  0  0  and  1  3  0  and  1  1
    1  0  0  and     9  0  and     6
  ──────────────────────────────────
    1  0  0  and     4  0  and     5
```

Answer: 145

or

```
      2    13   1
      3̶    4̶    1
−     1    9    6
    ──────────────
      1    4    5
```

Answer: 145

Multiplication

16 × 4 becomes

(10 × 4) + (6 × 4)

= 40 + 24

Answer: 64

or

×	4
10	40
6	24
Total	**64**

Answer: 64

or

$$
\begin{array}{r}
1\;6 \\
\times \quad 4 \\
\hline
4\;0 \\
2\;4 \\
\hline
6\;4 \\
\hline
\end{array}
$$

Answer: 64

Division

64 ÷ 4 becomes

(40 ÷ 4) + (24 ÷ 4)

= 10 + 6

Answer: 16

or

$$
\begin{array}{r}
6\;4 \\
-\;4\;0 \\
\hline
2\;4 \\
-\;2\;4 \\
\hline
0 \\
\hline
\end{array}
\qquad
\begin{array}{r}
1\;0\;\times\;4 \\
\hline
6\;\times\;4 \\
\hline
1\;6 \\
\hline
\end{array}
$$

Answer: 16

National standard in maths

The mark that each child gets in the test paper will be known as the 'raw score' (for example, '50' in 50/110). The raw score will be converted to a scaled score and children achieving a scaled score of 100 or more will achieve the national standard in that subject. These 'scaled scores' enable results to be reported consistently year-on-year.

The guidance in the table below shows the marks that children need to achieve to reach the national standard. This should be treated as a guide only, as the number of marks may vary. You can also find up-to-date information about scaled scores on our website: www.scholastic.co.uk/nationaltests

Total mark achieved	Standard
0–60	Has not met the national standard in mathematics for Year 3
61–110	Has met the national standard in mathematics for Year 3

Q	Answers	Marks
1	8	1
2	7	1
3	15	1
4	150	1
5	25	1
6	$\frac{2}{10}$	1
7	80	1
8	4	1
9	28	1
10	120	1
11	$\frac{5}{7}$	1
12	200	1
13	530	1
14	5	1
15	116	1
16	33	1
17	506	1
18	216 Award 1 mark for an incorrect answer but with a correct demonstration of an appropriate method.	2
19	200	1
20	0	1
21	47	1
22	521	1
23	25	1
24	155	1
25	$\frac{4}{12}$	1
26	963	1
27	144 Award 1 mark for a correct demonstration of an appropriate written method for long multiplication but with one arithmetic error.	2
28	245	1

■SCHOLASTIC National Curriculum SATs Tests

Q	Answers	Marks
29	51 Award 1 mark for a correct demonstration of an appropriate written method for short division but with one arithmetic error.	2
30	900	1
31	1049 Award 1 mark for an incorrect answer but with a correct demonstration of an appropriate method.	2
32	247	1
33	3	1
34	28	1
35	36	1
36	260	1
	Total	**40**

Q	Answers	Marks
1	$\frac{1}{2}$	1
2	Triangle — Square — Pentagon — Hexagon matched to shapes	1
3	70	1
4	14	1
5	700g	1
6	420	1
7	Two lines perpendicular to each other - they should cross each other at right angles.	1
8	36cm	1
9	21 days	1
10	24 Award 1 mark for an incorrect answer but with an attempt to multiply or list all possible combinations.	2
11	8 6	1 1
12	£256 phone circled £100	1 1

Q	Answers	Marks
13	A	1
	4mm	1
14	Triangular prism	1
	Cube	1
15	838 buttons	2
	Award 1 mark for an incorrect answer but with a correct demonstration of an appropriate written method for adding 100.	
16	327	2
	Award 1 mark for an incorrect answer but with a correct demonstration of an appropriate method.	
17	18	2
	Award 1 mark for a correct demonstration of an appropriate written method for short division but with one arithmetic error.	
18	One wheel/circle drawn for buses	1
	Scooter	1
19	$\frac{5}{12}$	2
	Award 1 mark for an incorrect answer but with a correct demonstration of an appropriate method for adding/subtracting fractions.	
20	865	2
	Award 1 mark for an incorrect answer but with a correct demonstration of an appropriate written method for addition.	
21	£2.73	2
	Award 1 mark for an incorrect answer but with a correct demonstration of an appropriate method.	
22	£2	2
	Award 1 mark for an incorrect answer but with a correct demonstration of an appropriate method.	
	Total	**35**

Q	Answers	Marks
1		1
2	4	1
3	800, 900, 1000	1
4	$\begin{array}{r} 9\,7\,1 \\ -\,\mathbf{4\,6}\,3 \\ \hline 5\,0\,8 \end{array}$	1
5	9:54pm	1
6	28kg	1
7	3 6 21 4	1
8	d	1
9	120	1
10	620. Accept final answer in words. Award 1 mark for an incorrect answer but with a correct demonstration of an appropriate written method for addition.	2
11	B 150ml	1 1
12	55 children Award 1 mark for an incorrect answer but with a correct demonstration of an appropriate method.	2
13	$\frac{3}{12}$ Award 1 mark for an incorrect answer but with a correct demonstration of an appropriate written method for subtracting fractions.	2

143

Q	Answers	Marks
14	£13	1
	£78	1
15	16p	2
	Award 1 mark for a correct demonstration of an appropriate written method for multiplication but with one arithmetic error.	
16	A reasonably accurate drawing of an isosceles triangle with one right angle and two sides of 7cm. Award 1 mark for a right-angled triangle but sides not of the correct length.	2
17	51, 55, 59, 63	1
	51, 47, 43, 39	1
18	$\frac{2}{9}$ Award 1 mark for an incorrect answer but with a correct demonstration of an appropriate written method for adding/subtracting fractions.	2
19	559 litres Award 1 mark for an incorrect answer but with a correct demonstration of an appropriate written method for subtraction.	2
20	789kg Award 1 mark for an incorrect answer but with a correct demonstration of an appropriate method.	2
21	102cm Award 1 mark for an incorrect answer but with a correct demonstration of an appropriate method.	2
22	144 Award 1 mark for an incorrect answer but with a correct demonstration of an appropriate method.	2
	Total	35

Q	Answers	Marks
1	25	1
2	16	1
3	18	1
4	15	1
5	800	1
6	11	1
7	$\frac{4}{5}$	1
8	45	1
9	72	1
10	66	1
11	17	1
12	15	1
13	380	1
14	291	1
15	9	1
16	196	1
17	$\frac{3}{6}$	1
18	455	1
19	$\frac{7}{8}$	1
20	600	1
21	193	1
22	550	1
23	579	1
24	8	1
25	88 Award 1 mark for an incorrect answer but with a correct demonstration of an appropriate method.	2
26	660	1
27	7	1

Q	Answers	Marks
28	841 Award 1 mark for an incorrect answer but with a correct demonstration of an appropriate method.	2
29	888	1
30	350	1
31	584 Award 1 mark for a correct demonstration of an appropriate method for long multiplication but with one arithmetic error.	2
32	100	1
33	$\frac{2}{9}$	1
34	147 Award 1 mark for a correct demonstration of an appropriate written method for short division but with one arithmetic error.	2
35	670	1
36	18	1
	Total	**40**

Q	Answers	Marks
1	40, 45, 50	1
2	Award 1 mark for five beads clearly marked off with a continuous, or near-continuous line.	1
3	$\begin{array}{r} 6\,4\,0 \\ +\,1\,8\,7 \\ \hline 8\,2\,7 \end{array}$	1
4	Accept 20 to three, 2.40pm, 14.40 or 14.40pm	1
5	$\frac{1}{3}$	1
6	11cm 9mm accept 119mm	1
7	b	1
8	669 Award 1 mark for an incorrect answer but with a correct demonstration of an appropriate written method.	2
9	144 Award 1 mark for an incorrect answer but with a correct demonstration of an appropriate written method for subtraction.	2
10	< > Both answers need to be correct to reward the mark.	1
11	77 raisins Award 1 mark for correct approach to written subtraction but with one arithmetic error.	2
12	$\frac{1}{8}, \frac{3}{8}, \frac{6}{8}, \frac{7}{8}$	1
13	18	1
	Oranges	1
14	Gemma	1
	2 minutes	1

Q	Answers	Marks
15	Has six square faces Has twelve edges and six rectangular faces Four of its faces meet at a vertex Has one curved face Has a circle for its base Has two triangular faces and three rectangular faces Award 1 mark if at least three are correct.	2
16	Charlie Award 1 mark for an incorrect answer but with a correct demonstration of an appropriate method.	2
17	6 chocolates Award 1 mark for an incorrect answer but with a correct demonstration of an appropriate method. Also award 1 mark if $\frac{3}{8}$ is given.	2
18	14g sugar 42g flour 28g butter Award 1 mark for two out of three correct.	2
19	473 cars Award 1 mark for correct approach to solving the problem but with one arithmetic error.	2
20	60cm Award 1 mark for an incorrect answer but with a correct demonstration of an appropriate method.	2

Q	Answers	Marks
21	86p Award 1 mark for an incorrect answer but with a correct demonstration of an appropriate method.	2
22	9°C	1
	6°C	1
	Total	**35**

SCHOLASTIC National Curriculum SATs Tests

Q	Answers	Marks
1	C	1
2	1	1
3	1 litre or 1000ml	1
4	56	1
5	40m	1
6	9	1
7	52p	1
8	396	1
9	Yes. 219 − 151 = 68 or 219 − 68 = 151	1
10	$\frac{1}{10}$, $\frac{2}{10}$, $\frac{3}{10}$, $\frac{5}{10}$, $\frac{9}{10}$	1
11	1 8 **7** + 4 5 ―――― 2 3 1	1
12		2
13	578	1
	340, 440	1
14	9	2
	Award 1 mark for a correct written method with one arithmetic error.	
15	A 6cm 4mm	1
	B 9cm 8mm	1
16	278	2
	Accept answer in words if calculation has been done correctly. Award 1 mark for a correct written method with one arithmetic error.	

Q	Answers	Marks
17	$\frac{3}{5}$ Award 1 mark for an incorrect answer but with a correct demonstration of an appropriate method.	2
18	a c	1 1
19	216 Award 1 mark for a correct demonstration of an appropriate written method for multiplication but with one arithmetic error.	2
20	430 Award 1 mark for an incorrect answer but with a correct demonstration of an appropriate written method for addition.	2
21	$\frac{1}{10}$ Award 1 mark for an incorrect answer but with a correct demonstration of an appropriate method for adding/subtracting fractions.	2
22	140 Award 1 mark for an incorrect answer but with a correct demonstration of an appropriate method.	2
23	95 litres Award 1 mark for an incorrect answer but with a correct demonstration of an appropriate written method for addition.	2
Total		**35**

■SCHOLASTIC National Curriculum SATs Tests

QUICK TESTS FOR SATs SUCCESS

BOOST YOUR CHILD'S CONFIDENCE WITH 10-MINUTE SATs TESTS

- Bite-size mini SATs tests which take just 10 minutes to complete
- Covers key National Test topics
- Full answers and progress chart provided to track improvement
- Available for Years 1 to 6

Find out more at www.scholastic.co.uk